CW00860078

A New Holiday

Sophia Stephens
and
Brian Owens

Published by Ada Cole Publishing
610 Wesley Ave, Ferguson, MO. 63135

A New Holiday: A Magical Christmas Story for Children Coping With Loss © All Rights reserved.

LION FORGE ANIMATION
Executive Producer: David Steward II
Producer: Susan Sordo
Illustrations by Binay Kumar Biswal
ISBN: 979-8-9871684-1-7

Inspired by the life of

Dr. Dorothy Elizabeth Massingale Steward
&
Thelma Elizabeth Steward

in loving memory of:

Mr. Harold Steward
Mrs. Dorothy Steward
Mr. Ellis Marsalis
Mrs. Dolores Marsalis
Mrs. Roberta Owens

'Twas the night before Christmas
and things were not the same,
for a little girl named Thelma
so many things had changed.

Christmas was coming!
Her favorite time of year.
A time full of family,
laughter and cheer.

But this season was different
for little Thelma, you see,
For the one gift she wanted
would not fit under the tree.

But much to her surprise
the best was yet to come.
A Christmas like no other
full of Hope, Joy, and Love.

"Dear God," Thelma prayed,
"So much has changed this year.
Since Grandma Dorothy's been gone,
I don't feel Christmas Cheer.

That's why this year for Christmas
what I want most of all
isn't a dress or a brand-new bike,
not even a baby doll.

Written in bold
at the top of my list
is for this Christmas
to really feel like Christmas."

Thelma jumped into bed
wondering if God would
hear her prayer.
Would she wake in the morning
and find Grandma Dorothy there?

She thought to herself,
"I guess I will see."
Then she closed her eyes
and was soon fast asleep.

When morning came
the sun was shining bright.
Thelma heard birds chirping
as she opened her eyes.

"It's Christmas! It's Christmas!"
Thelma joyfully said.
But she sensed something strange
as she jumped out of bed.

There was no laughter or music
not a sound or a peep,
no smell of Christmas breakfast,
everyone was still asleep.

So she dashed down the stairs
and what did she see?
No fire under the mantle
and no gifts under the tree.

"This doesn't feel like
Christmas at all,"
Thelma said with a sigh.
"I guess God didn't hear me."
But then something
caught her eye.

She saw a bright colored card
with letters trimmed in gold.
The name on it was Thelma,
written in bold.

It read, "Far beyond the clouds
is a place of peaceful mirth.
For sweet Thelma I now call down
a bit of heaven on earth."
signed,
Love

"What does this mean?"
She thought to herself,
while at the card she stared.
Just then, Thelma could sense
that someone else was there.

"Hello Thelma!"
said a woman
shimmering in green.
She looked like an angel,
mystical and serene.

"Who are you?" Thelma cried,
her heart filled with fear.
"And who let you in?
How did you get in here?"

"My name is Hope,"
the woman said with pride.
"I come from up north,
where happiness abides.

Hope asked as Thelma
looked on in fright,
"Don't you expect your prayers
to be answered?
I received an invite last night."

"Have we met before?"
Thelma asked Hope
dressed in green,
who now happily stood
next to the Christmas tree.

"I suppose never formally,
but we all know about you."

"We?" asked Thelma.

"Oh, you'll see very soon."

"Merry Christmas!" said Hope,
then Thelma thought
about her prayer.
"This is not a Merry Christmas,"
she replied in despair.

"Why is everyone still sleeping?"
Thelma asked in a tiff.
"Why doesn't this
feel like Christmas?
And why aren't there any gifts?"

"You can't see all these gifts?!"
Hope asked in surprise.
Thelma looked under the tree,
"There are no gifts in sight."

"Thelma, now I know why I'm here.
Where I come from
gifts are easily seen
and anything is possible,
if you just believe.

Now, it's hard to believe
why you simply don't see,
but you can get what you need
if you repeat after me.

What I believe is what I see!"

Thelma repeated the phrase,
"What I believe is what I see?"
But in her heart,
didn't feel that way.

"Yes! Don't you get it?
It means your
gifts are closer than you think.

Look around you," said Hope,
"Everything is within reach."

Hope twirled as she danced,
and the room began to change.
There was a band playing music,
and a fireplace bright with flames.

Thelma also began
to twirl and dance,
but still something was missing.
The only gift she wanted
was the one for whom she'd been
praying and wishing.

Suddenly, Thelma stopped dancing
and with tears in her
eyes proclaimed,
"This still doesn't feel like
Christmas.
Nothing is the same.

I even said the words
you told me to repeat,
and I still can't find
the one gift I want to see."

Hope leaned in
and said with a twinkle in her eye,
"Lift your head up sweet Thelma.
Joy will help you see the gift you
prayed to find.

If you wish to take a journey
and find the gift you cannot see,
recite again without a doubt
in your heart,
"What I believe is what I see."

So Thelma closed her eyes,
and with all of her might,
began to spin and speak the words,
Hope gave her to recite.

"What I believe is what I see."

"What I believe is what I see."

"What I believe is what I see."

She twirled and twirled,
for what seemed like forever.
Then suddenly, she stopped,
as if someone pulled a lever.

Thelma opened her eyes,
as wide as could be.
She saw candies and cakes,
and the most beautiful
Christmas tree.

It was as tall as the ceiling,
and as wide as the sky.
With gifts of every color,
shape, and size.

Just then, she heard a voice,
and felt a hand all at once.
"Come with me!" A little boy said.

And as they got closer to the tree,
Thelma saw more kids everywhere,
filled with laughter and glee.

Then she heard the
most beautiful voice say,
"Hey everyone!
We have a new friend!"
As they danced up and down
a staircase that seemed to
have no end.

"Welcome, Merry Christmas!
We're so glad you're here!
Hope said you would be coming,
in need of Christmas cheer.

Is something missing
from your wish list?
Well my name is Joy.
Here to grant your
deepest wish!

So don't worry! Rejoice!
You're in the right place.
Joy's got anything you want.
Any size, any color, any shape."

"Anything?" Thelma asked,
as Joy dashed to the tree.
"That's right!
So what do you want?"

But before Thelma could speak...

Joy began shuffling through
the gifts,
looking for the perfect fit.
"Now, where is it?" She thought.
"Nope, that's not it."

So Joy looked and looked,
and found the perfect match.
Then she handed Thelma
a box with a big bow attached.

As Thelma opened the box,
her smile became a frown.
"She looks sad," the children said,
as her head drooped down.

In the box she found a
black coat, with bright
buttons of red, and a hat that
would fit perfectly
upon her head.

Joy asked if she liked it,
wanting Thelma to be glad.
"Yes, but this reminds me of
someone special,
that's why I feel sad."

"It's okay I'll get you
another one!"
Joy replied with glee.
"But I know what I want,"
Thelma said,
"isn't under that tree."

"That's impossible!" Joy cried,
"Impossible you see!
I've got everything you
could want underneath my
Christmas tree."

"Unless it isn't something,
But someone that you need.
Like the special person
you were thinking of.
Are they the gift you want to see?"

Thelma nodded and replied,
"Yes, please, more than anything."

"When a present is
wrapped in the past," Joy explained,
unwrapping is in remembering
the joy we once claimed.
Now come along and sing after me.
And before you know it,
you'll begin to see."

Thelma sang and sang,
until the sound became clear.
And the more she sang,
she could hear another voice
coming near.
Familiar, calming,
and sweet to the ear.

"GRANDMA DOROTHY!"
Thelma cried, as she fell into her arms.
"Oh! You've been on an adventure
Grandma's voice was
tender and warm.

"You mean, you were watching
the whole time?" Thelma replied.
"Of course!" said Grandma Dorothy.
"Love is always watching,
it's what brought you to this side!"

"I've missed you so much
since you've gone away.
Nothing feels special without you,
not even Christmas day.

Can I stay here with you?"
Thelma pleaded with all her might.
Grandma Dorothy sweetly
answered,
"Well, that sure would be nice.

But if you stay here with me,
who will your mother read
bible stories to?
Who will go with your sister,
Deborah,
to the movies on
Sunday afternoons?

And I know Friendship
Missionary Baptist Church
will miss their most
valuable usher!"
Thelma hadn't thought about that,
and soon began to wonder.

"Sweet Thelma, change is never easy,
especially during the holidays.
But, there are some things in life
that will never go away.

Like hope and faith,
the heavens and the stars,
The power of love's creation,
and the gift that you are."

"You know, the way you feel
about me,
so many people feel about you!
Your eyes and your smile
light up the gloomiest rooms!

So keep shining for
Grandma Dorothy.
Keep shining your light
in this world,
and love will shine back on you.
That's what Christmas is all about,
baby girl."

"I'll miss you Grandma Dorothy,"
Thelma said with tears in her eyes.
For she knew in her heart,
her grandma was right.

Just then, Grandma Dorothy
pulled her in tight,
and gave her the biggest hug
she had ever had in her life.

"I'll miss you too sweet Thelma,
but don't worry my child,
because of love, you'll see me again
in the place where light
always shines.
Now close your eyes."

Thelma smiled as she did,
because this time she knew,
she'd see Grandma Dorothy again.

And just like that, Thelma awoke.
She was not in a dream.

For the sights and sounds
of Christmas
were beautiful, bright, and pristine.

The bedrooms were empty.
She thought, "Could it be?"
So she ran down the stairs,
wondering what she would see.

"Merry Christmas!" everyone said,
as they sat by the tree.
Her father and mother,
little sister and big brothers,
and Christmas gifts
that she could finally see.

And so the story continues,
with family gathered
around the tree.

A New Holiday, in which Thelma
has every gift she'll ever need.

The End

Meet the Authors

Sophia Stephens

Sophia Stephens is a singer, songwriter, actress and producer from St. Louis, Missouri. After relocating to New York to join the Tony Award-Winning Broadway musical, The Lion King, as the leading female role, 'Nala,' Sophia now resides in Los Angeles, California. There, she serves as the co-director of graduate programs for A BroaderWay Foundation, where she mentors young female artists and has taught songwriting for the past seven years. Her love of writing stems from her childhood, writing songs for her late grandmother's church. A New Holiday is Sophia's first book, co-written with author Brian Owens.

Brian Owens

Brian Owens is a Grammy-nominated artist, producer and co-author of his first book, A New Holiday, with Sophia Stephens. Born and raised in the St. Louis area, Brian grew up singing in the church where his father was a Pastor. His faith, along with his wife, their eight children and their local community of Ferguson, Missouri, represents the foundation upon which Brian has built his career. A graduate of the University of Missouri-St. Louis, Brian also serves as the music director and artist-in-residence at the World Chess Hall of Fame and founder of the Life Creative STL Ecosystem. Brian is a dedicated community facilitator and leader looking to build a world beyond his music.

Lightning Source UK Ltd.
Milton Keynes UK
UKHW050459080223
416583UK00003B/67